PLAY DRUMS

COLDPLAY

Published by
Wise Publications
14-15 Berners Street, London W1T 3LJ, England

Exclusive Distributors:
Music Sales Limited
Distribution Centre, Newmarket Road,
Bury St Edmunds, Suffolk IP33 3YB
Music Sales Pty Limited
20 Resolution Drive, Caringbah,
NSW 2229, Australia.

Order No. AM979869
ISBN 1-84449-465-9
This book © Copyright 2004 by
Wise Publications.

Compiled by Nick Crispin.
Music arranged by Paul Townsend
and Arthur Dick.
Music processed by Paul Ewers Music Design.
Cover designed by Fresh Lemon.
Cover photograph (Chris Martin) LFI,
(Will Champion) Bob King / Redferns.

Printed in the United Kingdom by
Printwise (Haverhill) Limited, Suffolk.

CD recorded, mixed and mastered by
Jonas Persson.
Guitars by Arthur Dick.
Bass by Paul Townsend.
Drums by Brett Morgan.
Piano by Paul Honey.

www.musicsales.com

Your Guarantee of Quality
As publishers, we strive to produce every
book to the highest commercial standards.
The music has been freshly engraved
and the book has been carefully designed
to minimise awkward page turns and to make
playing from it a real pleasure.
Particular care has been given to specifying
acid-free, neutral-sized paper made from
pulps which have not been elemental
chlorine bleached. This pulp is from farmed
sustainable forests and was produced with
special regard for the environment.
Throughout, the printing and binding have
been planned to ensure a sturdy, attractive
publication which should give years of
enjoyment. If your copy fails to meet our
high standards, please inform us and we will
gladly replace it.

WISE PUBLICATIONS
London / New York / Paris / Sydney / Copenhagen / Berlin / Madrid / Tokyo

CLOCKS

Words & Music by Guy Berryman, Jon Buckland, Will Champion & Chris Martin

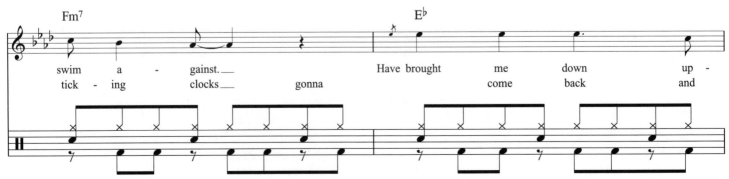

DON'T PANIC

Words & Music by Guy Berryman, Jon Buckland, Will Champion & Chris Martin

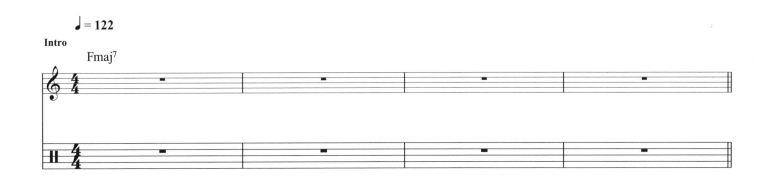

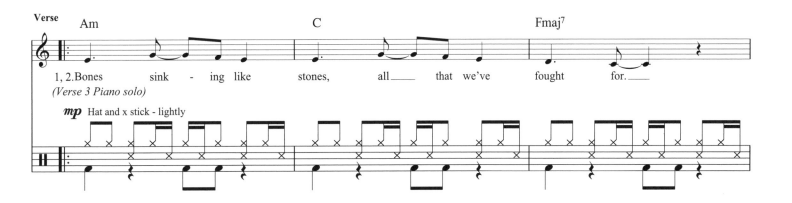

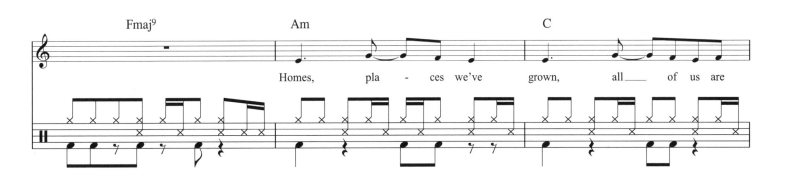

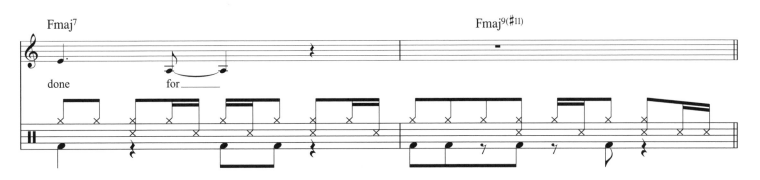

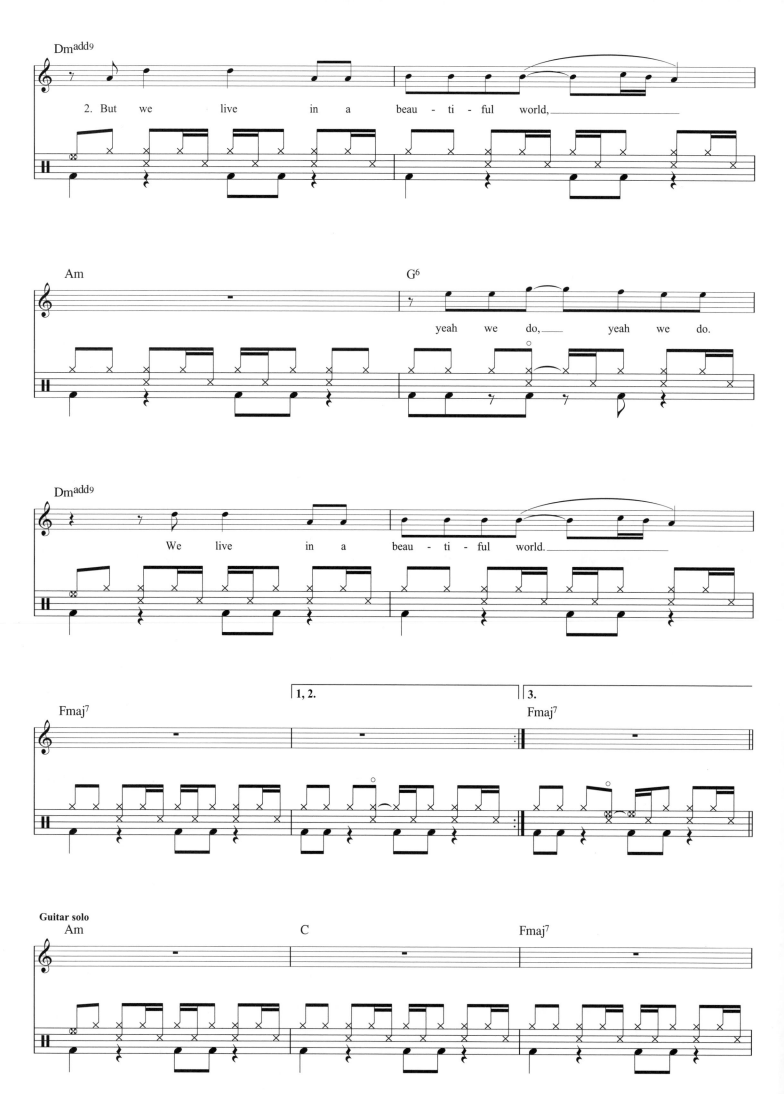

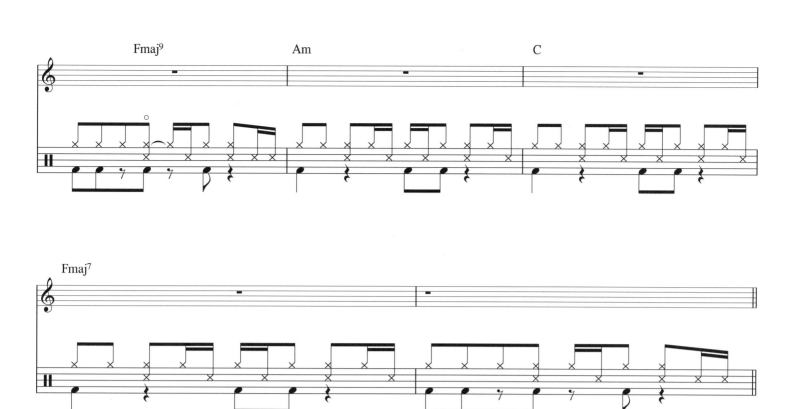

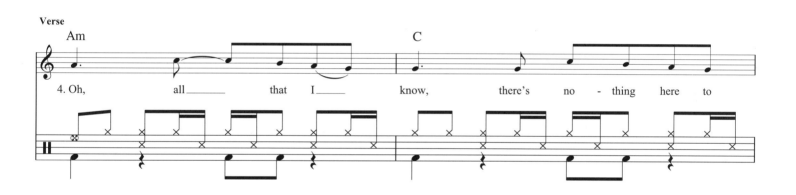

Verse

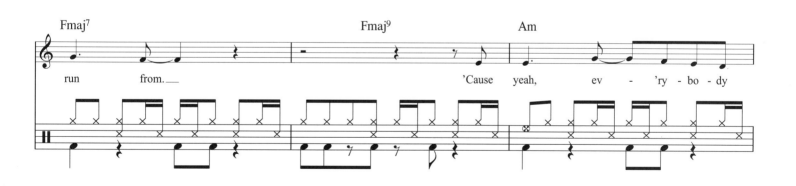

4. Oh, all_____ that I_____ know, there's no - thing here to run from._____ 'Cause yeah, ev - 'ry - bo - dy

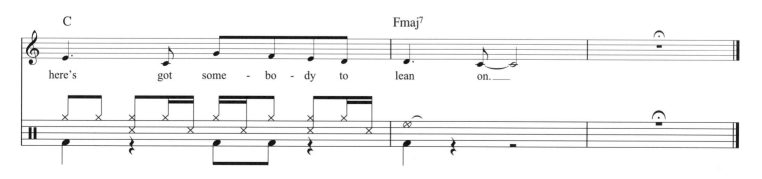

here's got some - bo - dy to lean on._____

EVERYTHING'S NOT LOST

Words & Music by Guy Berryman, Jon Buckland, Will Champion & Chris Martin

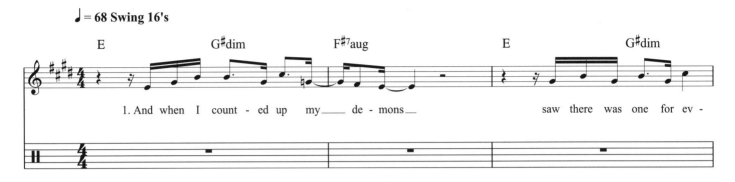

1. And when I count - ed up my___ de - mons___ saw there was one for ev -

- 'ry day.___ But with the good ones___ on___ my shoul - ders

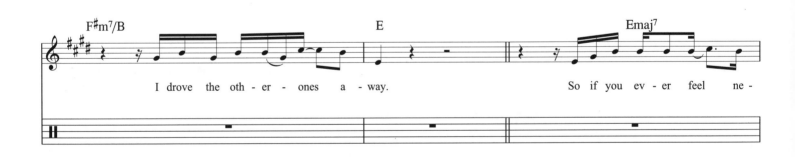

I drove the oth - er - ones a - way. So if you ev - er feel ne -

- glect - ed and if you think that all is lost,___ well, I'll be count - ing up my___

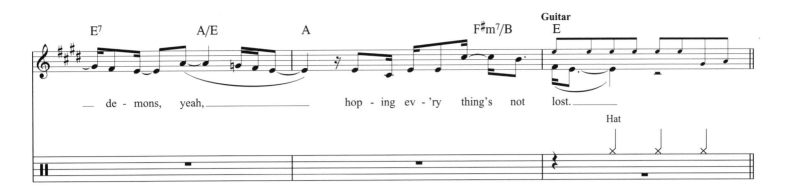

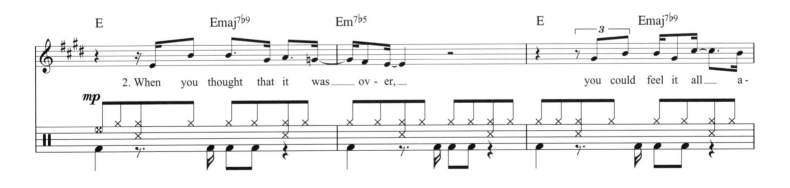

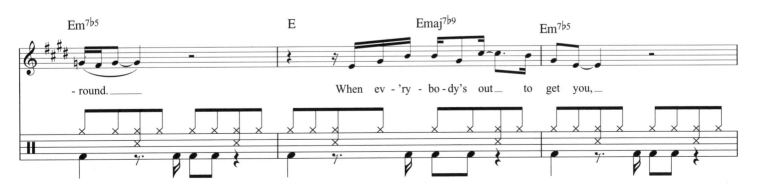

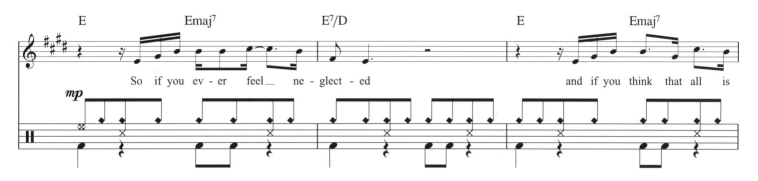

So if you ev - er feel__ ne - glect - ed   and if you think that all is

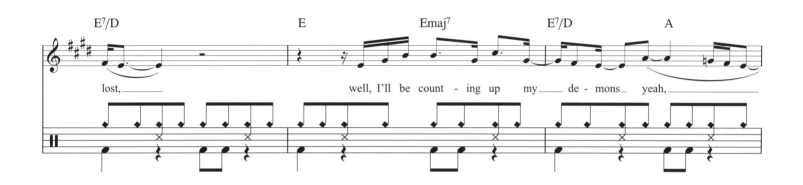

lost,_____   well, I'll be count - ing up my__ de - mons__ yeah,_____

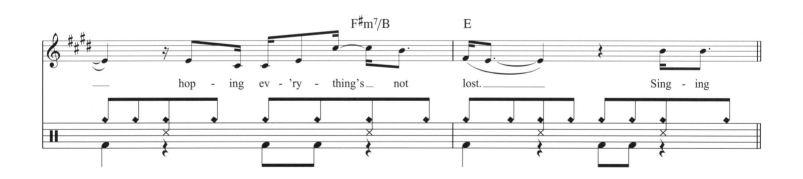

___ hop - ing ev - 'ry - thing's__ not   lost._____   Sing - ing

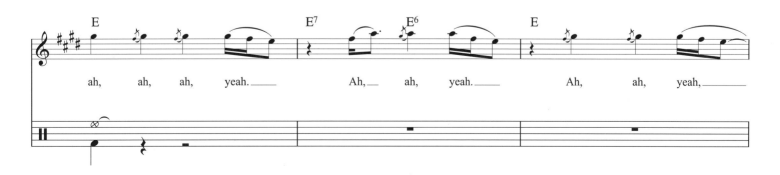

ah,   ah,   ah,   yeah._____   Ah,__   ah,   yeah.   Ah,   ah,   yeah,

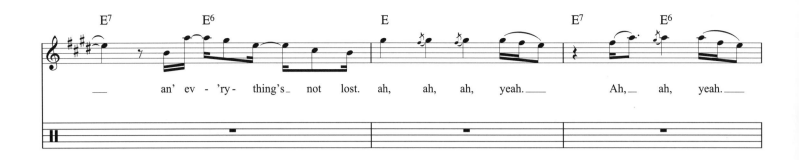

an' ev - 'ry- thing's_ not lost. ah, ah, ah, yeah. ___ Ah, __ ah, yeah. ___

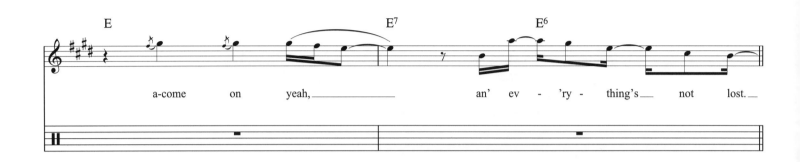

a-come on yeah, ___ an' ev - 'ry - thing's_ not lost. ___

Ah, ah, yeah. ___ Ah, ah, yeah. ___ Ah, ah, yeah, ___

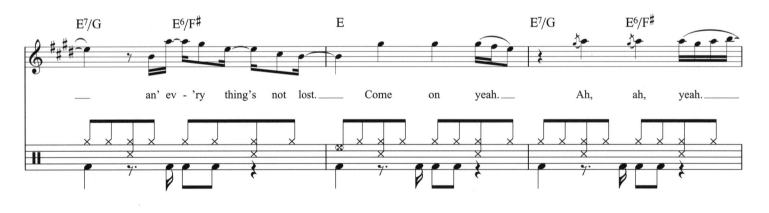

an' ev - 'ry thing's not lost. ___ Come on yeah. ___ Ah, ah, yeah. ___

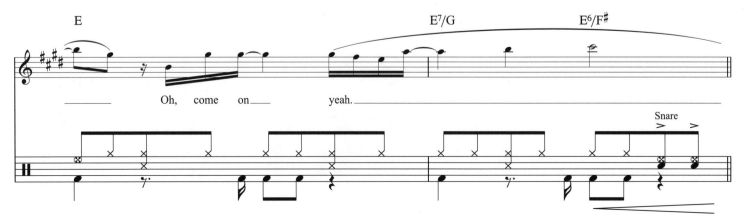

Oh, come on ___ yeah. ___

GOD PUT A SMILE UPON YOUR FACE

Words & Music by Guy Berryman, Jon Buckland, Will Champion & Chris Martin

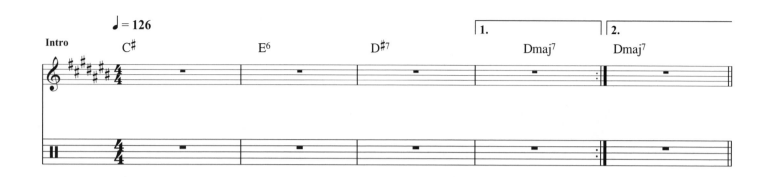

1. Where do we go, no - bo - dy knows!

I've got to say I'm on my way down.

God give me style and give me grace.

God put a smile up - on my face. _____

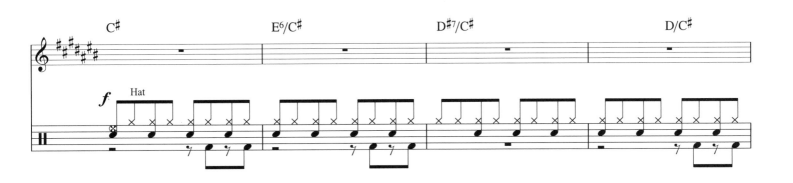

Verse

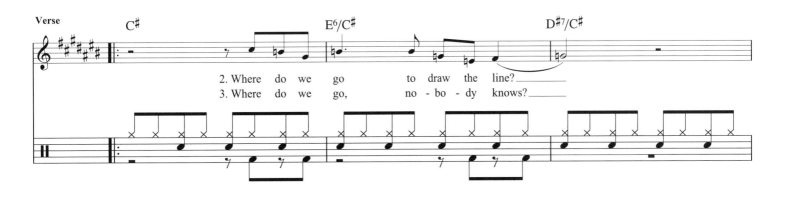

2. Where do we go to draw the line? _____
3. Where do we go, no - bo - dy knows? _____

I've got - ta say I've wast - ed all _____
Don't ev - er say you're on your way _____

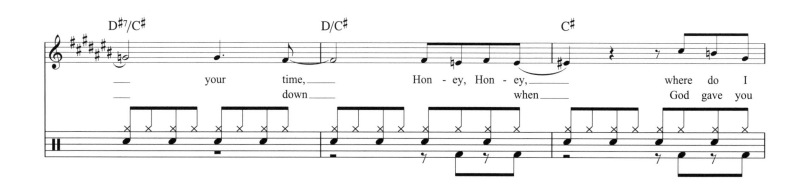

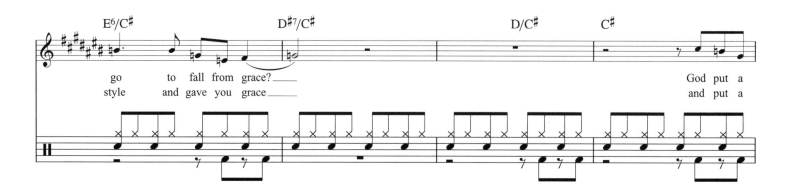

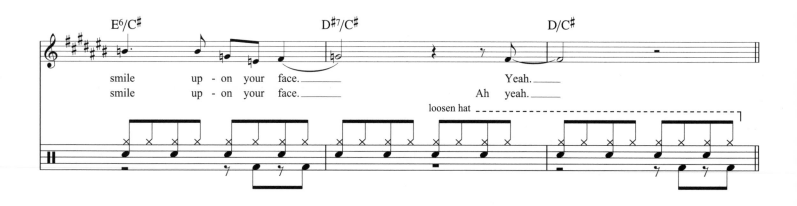

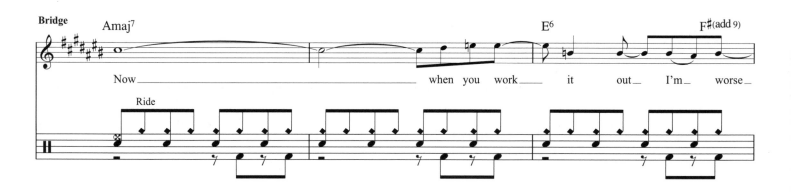

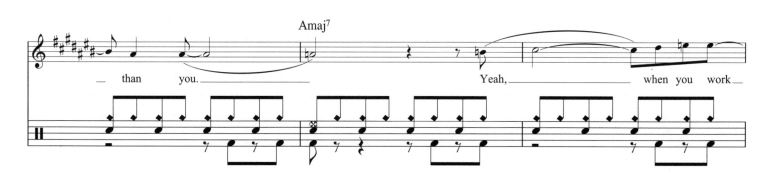

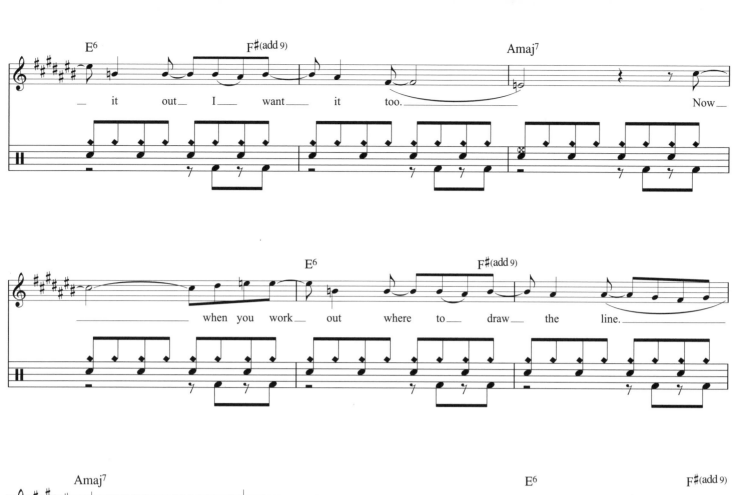

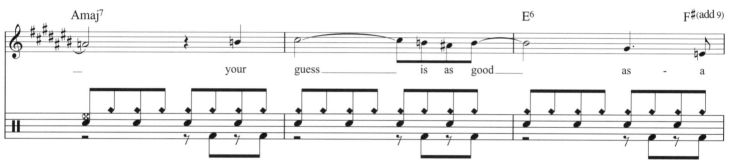

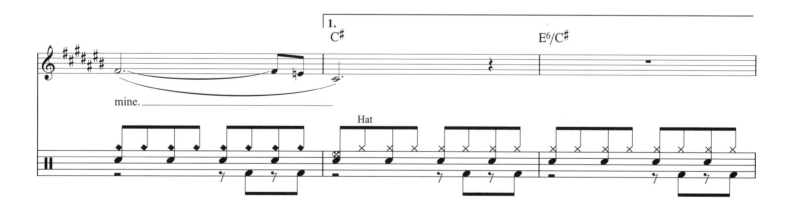

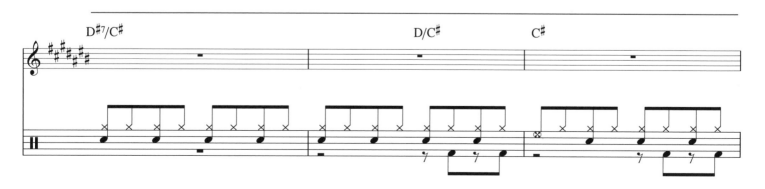

20

good as a mine. _____

Where do we go, no-bo-dy knows? _____

Don't ev-er say you're on your way _____ down _____ when _____

God gave you style and gave you grace _____

and put a smile up-on your face. _____

IN MY PLACE

Words & Music by Guy Berryman, Jon Buckland, Will Champion & Chris Martin

SHIVER

Words & Music by Guy Berryman, Jon Buckland, Will Champion & Chris Martin

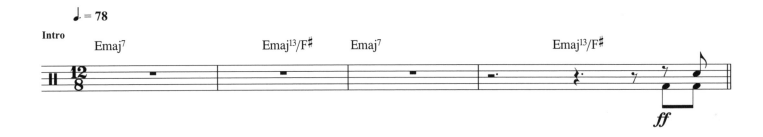

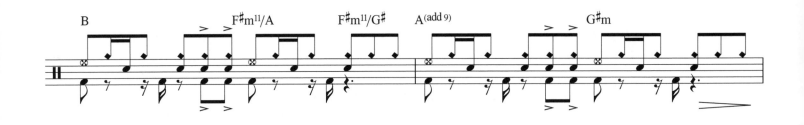

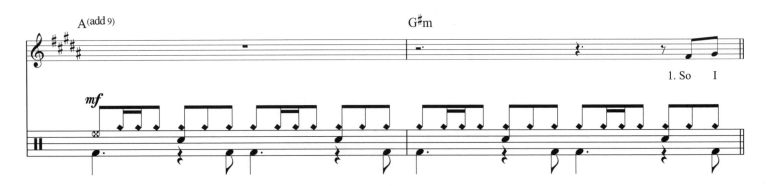

Yeah, I'll al - ways_ be wait - ing for you._

Yeah I'll al - ways_ be wait - ing for you._

Yeah I'll al - ways be wait - ing for you,_

_____ for _____ you, I will al - ways_ be wait - ing. And it's

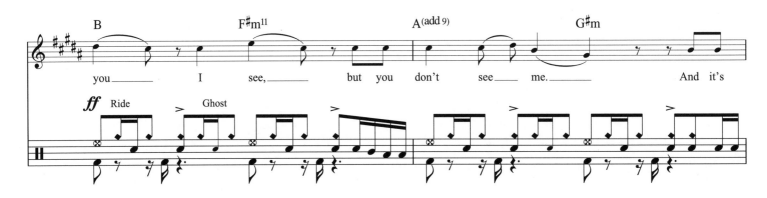

you _____ I see,_____ but you don't see_ me._____ And it's

TROUBLE

Words & Music by Guy Berryman, Jon Buckland, Will Champion & Chris Martin

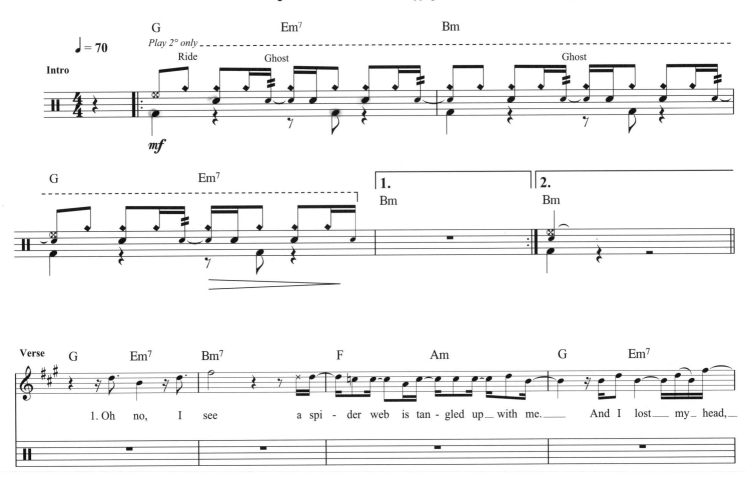

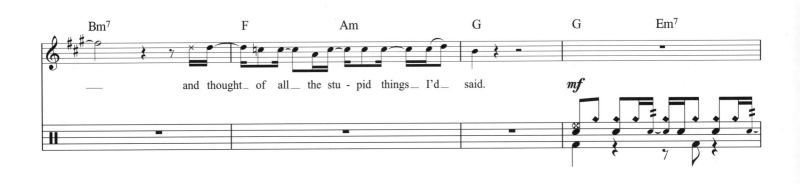

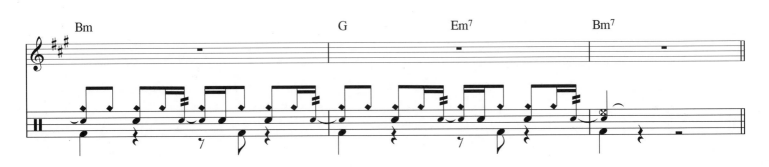

ah,_____ well if I ev - er caused___ you trou - ble,_____ then

To Coda ⊕

oh____ no, I nev - er meant to do____ you harm.____

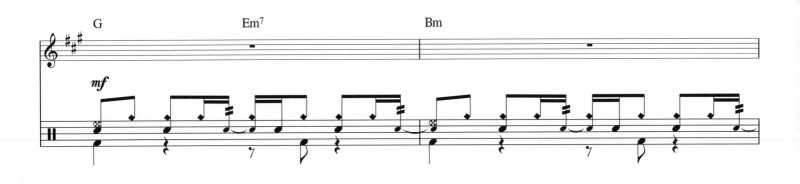

D.S. al Coda

⊕*Coda*

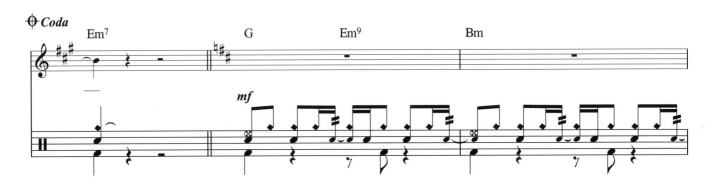

YELLOW

Words & Music by Guy Berryman, Jon Buckland, Will Champion & Chris Martin

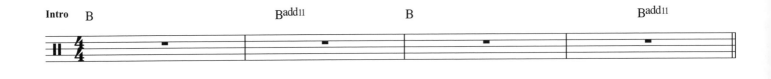

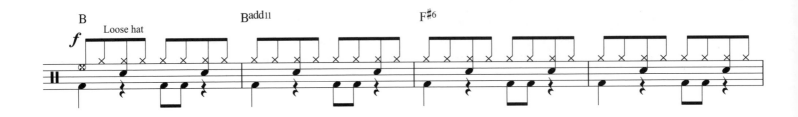

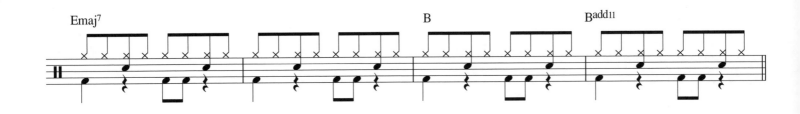

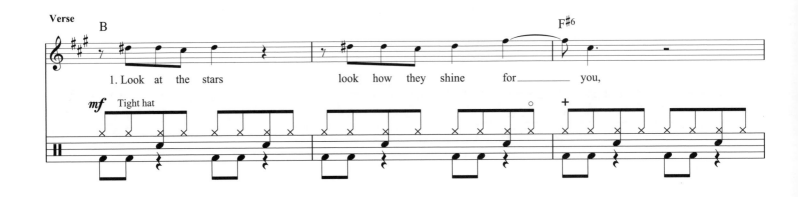

1. Look at the stars   look how they shine   for _____ you,

and ev - 'ry - thing you_ do,_____   yeah, they were all_ yel - low._

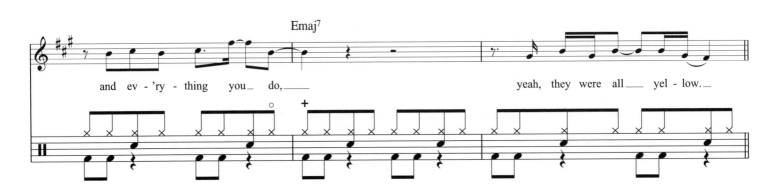

CD TRACK LISTING

FULL INSTRUMENTAL PERFORMANCES
(WITH DRUMS)…

1. CLOCKS

2. DON'T PANIC

3. EVERYTHING'S NOT LOST

4. GOD PUT A SMILE UPON YOUR FACE

5. IN MY PLACE

6. SHIVER

7. TROUBLE

8. YELLOW

BACKING TRACKS ONLY
(WITHOUT DRUMS)…

9. CLOCKS

10. DON'T PANIC

11. EVERYTHING'S NOT LOST

12. GOD PUT A SMILE UPON YOUR FACE

13. IN MY PLACE

14. SHIVER

15. TROUBLE

16. YELLOW

All tracks: Berryman/Buckland/Champion/Martin
BMG Music Publishing Limited.

To remove your CD from the
plastic sleeve, lift the small lip on the side
to break the perforated flap.
Replace the disc after use for convenient storage.